This book belongs to

_____

THE RUNT PIG
a collection of short stories

Color Edition

Copyright © 2019 by All About® Learning Press, Inc.
Previous editions copyright © 2010-2018
Printed in the United States of America

Color Edition
v. 2.1.0

All About® Learning Press, Inc.
615 Commerce Loop
Eagle River, WI 54521

ISBN 978-1-935197-72-0

Stories:
  Marie Rippel: "Tin Raft" – "Lost in the Bog" – "Lunch" – "The Big Top"
                       "Slim Went West" – "The Hit" – "Mud Milk" – "The Ant Hill"
                       "The Plan" – "The Big Mess" – "The Runt Pig" – "Fish Class"
                       "Fun at the Pond" – "The Long Nap"

  Renée LaTulippe: "The Pet Duck" – "The Bat and King Sam" – "Frank Shrank"
                       "At Camp"

Illustrations:
  Matt Chapman: "The Big Top" – "The Hit" – "The Runt Pig"

  Donna Goeddaeus: "Tin Raft" – "Lost in the Bog" – "Lunch" – "Slim Went West"
                       "Mud Milk" – "The Ant Hill" – "The Plan" – "The Big Mess"
                       "Fun at the Pond" – "The Long Nap" – "At Camp"

  Dave LaTulippe: "Fish Class" – "The Pet Duck" – "The Bat and King Sam"
                       "Frank Shrank"

Contributors: Donna Goeddaeus, Samantha Johnson

Cover Design: Dave LaTulippe

Page Layout: Andy Panske

Colorization of Stories: Donna Goeddaeus

The Runt Pig: a collection of short stories is part of the
All About® Reading program.

For more books in this series, go to www.AllAboutReading.com.

To the reader—
enjoy your trip through this book!

Contents

Tin Raft

Kent held his tin raft.

It was bent.

It had rust. It had a dent.

Can Tish fix it?

Tish set it on the bench.

Tish can sand it, bend it,

and mend it.

It was a big task.

But Tish did the job.

Tish had Kent test the raft
in the tub.
It did not tilt!

It was the best gift!

The End

Lost in the Bog

Gump was lost in the bog
at dusk.

Gump felt the mist.

Gump felt the wind.

But Gump went on.

Gump felt a bump.

It went past.

It was fast. Gasp!

Gump hid.

Is it a dog?

Is it a pest?

Is it an elf?

Is it ... the end?

Gump must act fast.

Gump can run! That is it!

Gump ran fast.

A big bump

is on the path!

Help!

But the bump is just Sis!

The End

Lunch

Is that lunch?

The chimp must get that bunch!

It is just a hop, skip, and a jump.

Jump!

Swish!

SNAP!

Did the bunch drop?

YES!

Did the chimp spin?

YES!

The chimp has a bump, a lump,

and a limp!

But the chimp has lunch!

Chomp! Gulp! Munch!

The End

The Big Top

The tent is up.

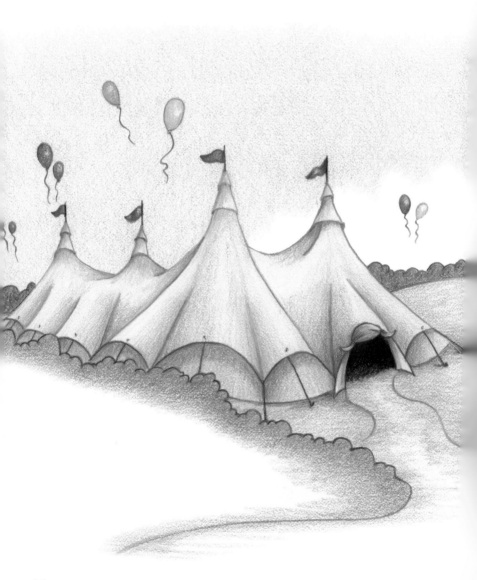

Step in! Get a spot!

Clem hits the drum.

Bam! Bam! Bam!

Glen gets the flag.

Swish!

Stan and Liv spin.

Mel and Flash jump!

Fran and Brad get on top!

Clip, clop! Clip, clop!

Gus and Spot run fast!

Ten men jump, skip, and flip.

A trip to the Big Top
is fun!

The End

Slim Went West

The West was a vast land.

Slim had just a map

and a hat.

Slim can get rich in the West!

Slim left on the trip

with the map in his hand.

Is that a red rag?

This rag can help on the trip
to the West.

The rag can stop the dust.

The red rag is a lunch bag

at the end of a twig.

It is hot.

The rag can stop the sun.

A dog is lost. His leg has a cut.

Slim can help the dog

with the rag.

The dog can help Slim.

The dog can get an ax.

Slim can chop a log

with the ax.

The sun has set.

Slim must stop and rest.

The dog and Slim
get in this tent.

Slim had his hat, a map, a rag,

a tent, an ax, and a dog.

Slim *was* rich.

The End

The Hit

Fred is up at bat.

Can Fred hit it?

SMASH!

It is a big hit!

Fred is a champ!

It went up and up.

It did not land!

Can Fred and his pals spot it?

Did it thud on the shed?

It is not on the shed.

Did it drop in the sand?

It is not in the sand.

Is it in the mulch?

It is not in the mulch.

Did it land in the dog dish?

It is not in the dog dish.

Fred and his pals

did not spot it.

Sh! It is in the nest!

The End

Mud Milk

Drop this shell in the glass

and add a bit of grass.

Toss in this stem and that grit.

This fluff will fit!

Cut up a red bud.

Add a glob of mud.

A snip of mint—such zest!

A bit of twig—that is best.

Drop in this and that. Plop!

Fill the glass to the top.

Mix in a bit of sand.

It is the best milk in the land!

Mix up a *lot!*

Mud milk hits the spot!

The End

The Ant Hill

The ant dug a path in the sand.

The ant did not rest.

It was a big job,
but the ant had help.

"Get the sand up the hill!"

said a big ant.

The ants left the sand

at the top.

The ants did not get lost.

"The hill will get big fast!"

said the ants.

Huff! Puff! Dig!

The ants had to dump
a lot of sand.

A bit fell off!

"Get a grip on that grit!"

said the big ant.

"Pass that sand up!"

said the ants.

The hill went up, up, up.

It was a big job,

but the ants did it!

The End

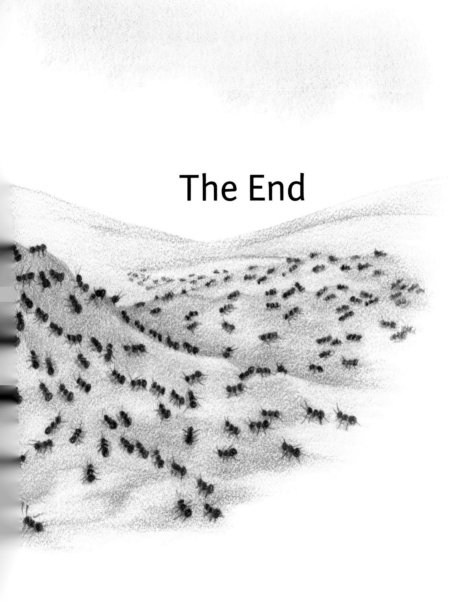

The Plan

Ann got a bed.

Gram has a plan

for a gift for Ann.

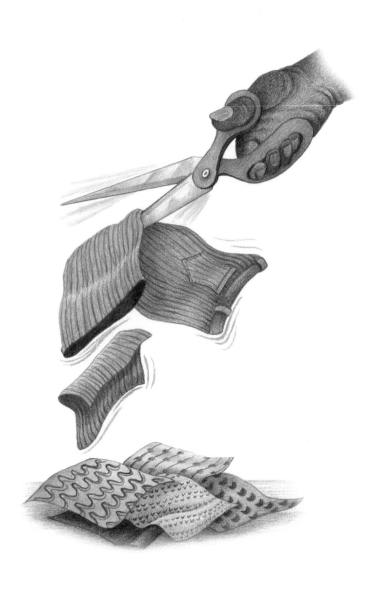

"I will cut up a dress
and a pant leg," said Gram.

"I will cut up a cloth bag
and a bit of soft silk."

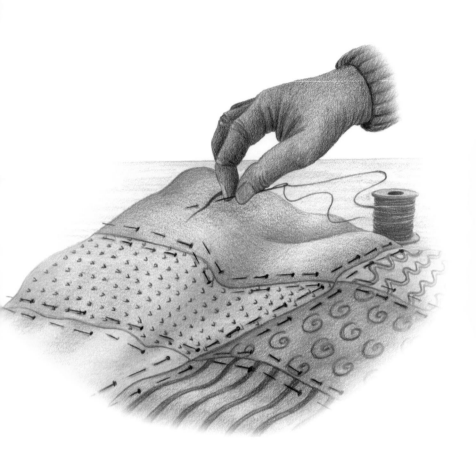

"I will mend a rip.

I will pin and snip."

"Next, I must press it,"

said Gram.

"It is a quilt!" said Ann.

"It is for the bed!"

The End

The Big Mess

Chen has a mix.

Chen will mix it up in a pot.

Chen will add milk.

Chen will add an egg.

Drop, drip, glop!

Chen will flip it in a pan.

Slip, slop, plop!

If the stuff gets stiff,
Mom will get mad.

Get a wet rag.
Get a damp mop.
Blot it. Mop it.
Get that big, wet mess!

It is still a mess!

Get that drip.

Get that drop.

Chen will not stop.

Chen will not miss a spot.

127

Chen did the job well,

and Mom is glad.

The End

The Runt Pig

Bret was a runt pig.

Was Bret fat? No.

Bret was slim.

Was Bret big? No.

Bret was just a runt.

Plop.

Bret hid in the mud pit.

Bret was sad.

Flap, flap, flap!

"A rat is in the hen hut!

The rat will get the egg!"

said Hen.

"Nell, help us! Get the rat!"

said Hen.

"But I will not fit
in the hen hut!" said Nell.

"Help us, Gruff! Lend us a hand!

Get the rat!" said Hen.

"But I will not fit

in the hen hut!" said Gruff.

"Fluff, lend us a hand!

Help us, or the rat

will get the egg!"

said Hen.

"But I will not fit

in the hen hut!"

said Fluff.

"Get Bret the Runt Pig!"

Hen said to Fluff.

"Bret will fit! Bret can run

up the ramp and get the rat!"

Fluff ran to get Bret.

"Bret, help us!

A rat is in the hen hut. The rat

will get the egg!" said Fluff.

"I will stop him," said Bret.

In a flash,

the runt pig sped up the path.

Bret ran to the hen hut

and then up the ramp.

The rat sat in the nest

next to the egg.

Bret hit the rat. Bop!

The rat ran.

Hen said,

"The rat has fled!

The egg is still in the nest!

Bret fit up the ramp

and lent us a hand."

Bret is not big,

but Bret can still help.

The runt pig is not sad.

The End

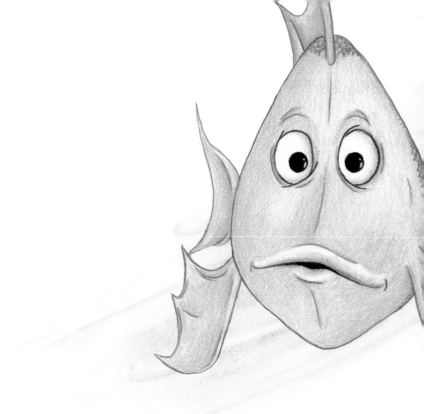

Fish Class

The fish swim to class.

The fish sit in math class.

"If a net dips in the pond, swim to the hut—fast!" said Miss Flip.

Class #2

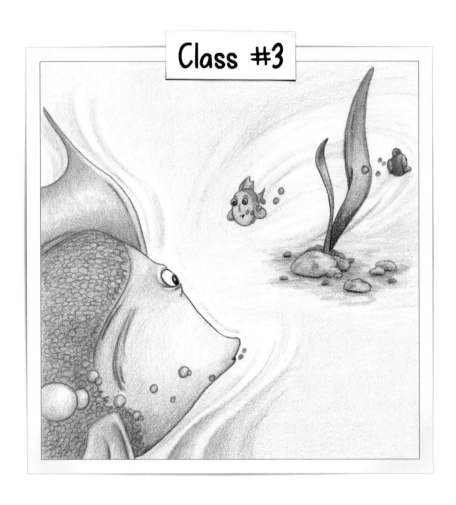

Class #3

The fish swim laps

to get fit and trim.

The fish jump up for fun.

Miss Flip said, "This is
a big, bad cat. If the cat gets
next to us, zig and zag.
This cat will get us if it can!"

Class #5

This is the best class.

The fish tug the bell

to get fed!

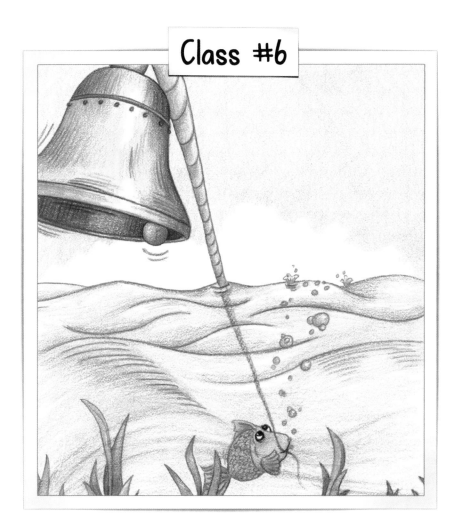

Class #6

At the end of class,

the fish nap.

The End

The Pet Duck

Quinn has a pet duck

with a black top hat.

Rick is a fun duck

but a bit bad!

Rick is quick

and can dash fast

in the grass!

Rick can run and slip.

Quinn gets wet!

The pet duck can sled
on a hill.

Rick the duck

can swim in the well.

Rick can grab a soft doll
with his bill.

Rick is glad.

Rick is *not* glad

to kick a rock.

At six on the dot,

Rick can quack and quack.

Then Quinn gets a snack

for him—a bit of jam

and a glass of milk!

At last, the duck naps

with Quinn.

Yes, Rick is a bit bad.

But Rick is still

the best pet duck!

The End

Fun at the Pond

Jill held the wet frog.

Jill set the frog

in the damp sand.

"Hop back to the
pond!" said Jill.

Hop, hop, hop.

The frog swam

past a fish to a pad.

The frog got on top of the pad
to bask in the sun.

A bug went past.

Dan dug in the sand

with a cup.

Dan dug a big pit.

Ben sat in the sand pit.

"Fill the pit with lots of
sand!" said Dan.

But Ben was still in it!

"Is Ben stuck in the sand?"

said Jill.

"No, I spot his leg

and his hand!" said Dan.

Ben got up with a grin.

"I spot a raft!" Ben said.

Dan ran to get a net,

and Jill got a stick.

Jill, Ben, and Dan

sat on the raft.

"Sh! Is it a fish?"

said Jill.

"That is not a fish," said Dan.

"Get it with the net!"

"It is quick! It dug in the muck

next to the log,"

said Ben.

"A trip to the pond

is fun," said Jill.

The End

The Bat and King Sam

This is King Sam.

His dog and cat ran off.

His pig and ox left.

It is just him and the wind
on the cliff.

The king is such a sad man.

King Sam can just sit
next to the lamp
and sob. Sniff!

But then ... is that a wing?

It *is* a wing! It is a thin bat!

The bat has to cling to a twig.

This bat is lost!

"Is that a soft hum?"

said King Sam.

Yes! This bat can sing!

It is a long, sad song. At the end,

the bat gets a big hug ...

and a big snack!

The bat has a plan.

The king will ring a bell

and the bat will sing a song.

Then the bat will get a snack!

It is not just the king and the wind
on the cliff.
The king has a pal,
and the bat can sing a glad song.

The End

The Long Nap

The best spot

for a long nap

is next to a log.

A moth went past, then six.

A finch sat on its nest.

It sang a song.

A red fox ran to his den ...

... and the cub went on

with his long nap.

A big web was spun.

A wet frog clung

to the log.

A bug fell off a twig.

Then the bug stung the cub.

Bad bug! Stop that!

And that was the end

of the long nap.

The End

Frank Shrank

A glass of pink milk
was on the desk.
Yum! Frank drank it.

And then Frank shrank ...

and shrank ...

and shrank!

Frank had such fun!

Frank hung on a mug ...

... and fell in a drop of pop.

Fizz!

A map led Frank
on a long path,
but Frank did not get lost.

At the end of the map was a web.

Such luck!

Frank swung on the thick web.

Then Frank slid on a stick.

It was fun to zip

past the lamp

on the back of a moth.

Honk, honk!

The wind of the fan was fast.

Crash!

Frank fell off the moth!

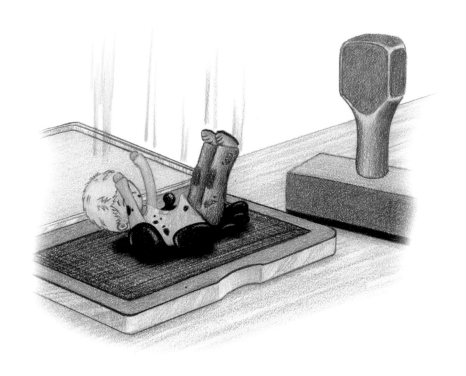

Thud! Frank sank

in a soft pad of ink.

"It was fun to shrink,"

said Frank, "but I think

I will drink that last drop

of pink milk."

Frank is big!

Frank is glad.

The End

At Camp

Jack and Hank

went up the hill to camp.

"Is that a fox?" said Jack.

"It is!" said Hank.

A red fox was on the path!

The sun was hot.

Jack sat in the grass to rest.

The fox was in no rush.

Hank and Jack

set up the tent.

Jack went to fish on the bank.

Yank!

Jack got a fish!

The fish fell off the dish!

Thud!

The fox got up to grab it.

The fox ran off with the fish.

Get him!

The fish was lost!

But Hank had a plum

and Jack had a fig.

Not bad!

"Off to bed," said Jack.

"Zip up the tent!" said Hank.

It was fun to camp on a hill.

The End

You did it!

You read the whole book!

What do you think of that?

Now it's time to read

Cobweb the Cat!